A Solution to

THE MARRIAGE MESS

By Jack T. Chick

Illustrated by
Fred Carter

CHICK PUBLICATIONS
P.O. Box 662
Chino, Calif. 91710

MY DEEPEST APPRECIATION TO .....

My lovely wife, Lynn.
Pastor James L. Franklin
Dr. Lloyd T. Anderson

and my great staff for all their help.

Also a special thanks to ....

JoAnn Cash Yates, who read the discarded manuscript of "The Marriage Mess" and talked me into publishing it.

Published by Chick Publications
P.O. Box 662, Chino, Calif. 91710
Printed in the United States of America
Printed by El Camino Press, LaVerne, California

WHEN GOD SAID TO EVE ... "WHAT IS THIS THAT THOU HAST DONE?" (GENESIS 3:13) HE ALREADY KNEW THE HORRIFYING CHAIN REACTION OF PROBLEMS THAT THEIR ACT OF REBELLION HAD CAUSED.

WARS, TORTURE, PERVERSION, DESPAIR, SUFFERING, LONELINESS, HATE, DISEASE, FEAR, SICKNESS, CONFUSION, DEATH AND HEARTBREAK SPREAD ACROSS HUMANITY LIKE GIANT SPIDERWEBS ENTANGLING ALL OF OUR LIVES.

TODAY CHRISTIAN HOMES ARE BEING BATTERED BY THE FORCES OF DARKNESS.

IT WOULD BE THE HEIGHT OF PRESUMPTION TO SAY THAT THIS BOOK HAS ANSWERS TO MOST OF THE COMPLEX PROBLEMS IN OUR HOMES; BUT, IF ONE LITTLE RAY OF TRUTH COULD IMPROVE YOUR FAMILY LIFE, THEN THIS LITTLE BOOK WAS WELL WORTH WHILE.

J.T.C.

CONTENTS

CHAPTER ONE

THE FRIENDLY FANATIC

OH, PASTOR . . . THAT WAS A BEAUTIFUL SERMON . . . WE'LL BE BACK TONIGHT! OH, I JUST REMEMBERED, MY COUSIN IS COMING TO VISIT US TOMORROW.

HE WAS A MISSIONARY FOR SEVENTEEN YEARS IN AFRICA . . . HE'LL BE WITH US FOR ONE MONTH. HE HAS SOME BUSINESS TO TAKE CARE OF.
I'D LIKE TO MEET HIM, MRS. MILLER.
YOU WILL! I'M SO PROUD OF HIM!

AND HE'S SINGLE! . . . MARTHA, YOU MUST MEET HIM WHEN HE COMES. I GUESS HE DOESN'T KNOW MANY WHITE WOMEN!
OH, HELEN, HE SOUNDS LIKE A WONDERFUL MAN!
COME ON, MATCH-MAKER! I'VE GOT TO GET HOME BEFORE THE GAME STARTS.

THE NEXT DAY

HEY, MAW—HOW DID HIS WIFE DIE IN AFRICA? DID THE CANNIBALS EAT HER?
HAW HAW—YOU MEAN LIKE MISSIONARY STEW?
NO, BRAD! . . . SHE DIED OF SOME KIND OF JUNGLE FEVER!

LET'S GET GOING OR WE'LL BE LATE . . . SANDY! . . . YOU'RE ALWAYS THE LAST ONE IN THE CAR . . . MOVE IT!!!
OH, SHUT UP, DADDY! MOM . . . MAKE HIM STOP PICKING ON ME!
I DON'T SEE WHY I HAVE TO GO MEET THIS OLD CREEP . . . HE'S YOUR RELATIVE! I DON'T WANNA GO!
@!!✷! SANDY . . . STOP TELLING ME TO SHUT UP . . . I'M YOUR FATHER!
BIG DEAL!
OH, DEAR . . . OH, DEAR . . .

I'M SO ASHAMED OF YOUR LONG HAIR, BILLY . . . HE'LL PROBABLY THINK YOU'RE A GIRL!
SHUT UP, MOM . . . I DON'T LIKE HIM ALREADY.
BOY, THAT'S A CUTE STEWARDESS . . . ARE THEY ALL LIKE THAT?

MARK . . . IS THAT REALLY YOU?
YES, HELEN . . . HOW NICE OF YOU TO MEET ME!
BOY . . . HE SURE IS OLD!

HELEN, THE LORD HAS GIVEN YOU A LOVELY FAMILY!
HI, MARK . . . I'M BILLY!
MY PLEASURE, BILLY!
HUMMM, HE DIDN'T SAY ANYTHING ABOUT MY HAIR . . . THAT'S COOL!

I'M SANDY!
HI, SANDY . . . YOU'RE A LOVELY YOUNG LADY!
I'LL BLOW HIS MIND WITH THIS ONE!

I HEAR THE CANNIBALS ATE YOUR WIFE!
OH, MY GOD! . . . (GASP) BRAD, HOW COULD YOU!
NO, BRAD! . . . THE LORD TOOK HER HOME WITH A FEVER!

*A man's gift maketh room for him. PROV. 18:16

BILLY, I HEARD YOU WERE ENGAGED SO I BROUGHT A LITTLE GIFT FOR YOUR SWEETHEART!
WOW . . . THANKS!
THIS IS GREAT! . . . I'M GONNA SHOW IT TO THE GUYS AT SCHOOL!
MARK! . . . YOU REALLY SHOULDN'T HAVE . . . THEY'RE SO BEAUTIFUL!

BRAD, IT'S TIME YOU GOT TO BED!
AWWW, COME ON, MAW!
DON'T GIVE ME ANY OF YOUR LIP, YOUNG MAN!
BRAD . . . SHUT UP! YOU LISTEN TO YOUR MOTHER!

EXCUSE ME, BUT COULDN'T WE HAVE PRAYER FIRST? . . . AND THANK GOD FOR ALL HE'S DONE TODAY?
GULP!
WHAT?
IT ISN'T SUNDAY!
WHAT'S WRONG WITH THIS GUY? HEY . . . I DON'T LIKE THIS!

DEAR FATHER, THANK YOU FOR YOUR LOVE AND FOR THE LORD JESUS! . . . THANK YOU FOR BRINGING ME HERE . . . I PRAY THAT THIS HOME WILL BE A LIGHT SHINING IN THE DARKNESS FOR YOU!
THIS IS HUMILIATING!
HOPE HE MAKES IT SHORT!
GOOD GRIEF . . . I HOPE HE DOESN'T CALL ON ME TO PRAY!

WHAT KIND OF WIERDOS DO YOU HAVE FOR RELATIVES?
I DIDN'T KNOW HE WAS A FANATIC!
HIS MONTH'S STAY WILL *PROBABLY* BE A NIGHTMARE!
I WONDER HOW WE CAN GET RID OF HIM?

CHAPTER TWO

SOUP'S ON!

NEXT MORNING
GOOD MORNING, HELEN . . . I'M SORRY I OVERSLEPT . . . THE TIME CHANGES ON MY FLIGHT FROM AFRICA GOT MY SLEEPING HABITS ALL MESSED UP!
HUMMPH! . . . I'VE BEEN WAITING TO COOK YOUR BREAKFAST *ALL* MORNING. NOW I'M LATE FOR MY HAIR DRESSER! . . . SO *YOU'RE* GOING TO HAVE TO MAKE YOUR *OWN* BREAKFAST . . . THE HOUSE IS A MESS, BUT I'M TOO BUSY!
I'LL SEE YOU LATE THIS AFTERNOON!

'BYE, HELEN . . . WHEN YOU'RE AT THE HAIR DRESSER DON'T FORGET TO LIFT UP THE LORD!
I'LL PRETEND I DIDN'T HEAR THAT! . . . *WHAT* DOES HE THINK I AM?

Whether therefore ye eat, or drink, or whatsoever ye do, do all to the glory of God.
1 COR. 10:31

And whatsoever ye do in word or deed, do all in the name of the Lord Jesus, giving thanks to God and the Father by him. COL. 3:17

4 P.M.
HEY . . . WHAT HAPPENED TO THE HOUSE?
IT LOOKS LIKE MOM FINALLY GOT WITH IT!
HEY . . . I WOULDN'T MIND BRINGING MY FRIENDS HOME NOW!

5 P.M.
WHAT'S THE MATTER, HELEN?
I . . . I FEEL SICK, MARK. I THINK I'M GETTING THE FLU!

SANDY . . . HELP YOUR MOTHER TO UNDRESS AND PUT HER TO BED, PLEASE!
OKAY, MARK!
HEY . . . WHAT ABOUT DINNER?
DON'T WORRY ABOUT IT, BRAD . . . I'LL TAKE CARE OF IT!

I'M STARVED . . . WHAT'S FOR DINNER, MARK?
WHAT WOULD YOU LIKE, FRANK?
DIDN'T HELEN MAKE IT YET? WHAT'S THE MATTER WITH HER?
SHE'S SICK!

SICK?? . . HOW IN BLAZES ARE WE GOING TO GET DINNER TONIGHT? MY STUPID DAUGHTER DOESN'T KNOW HOW TO COOK!
NEITHER DO YOU!
OOHH GOD, I HATE HIM!
FRANK . . . YOU AND I WILL HAVE THE PRIVILEGE OF PREPARING A LOVELY DINNER TONIGHT!

ARE YOU OUT OF YOUR MIND? I'VE NEVER COOKED DINNER OR WASHED DISHES OR DONE HOUSEWORK SINCE I'VE BEEN MARRIED . . . THAT'S WOMEN'S WORK!
I'M SORRY. I THOUGHT YOU WERE A CHRISTIAN!
I AM!

*JOHN 21:4-13 **JOHN 1:1, 2, 3, & 14

FRANK . . . WOULD YOU PLEASE MAKE THE SALAD?
I DON'T KNOW HOW!
I'LL HELP YOU!

FRANK, DID YOU EVER HEAR ABOUT HUDSON TAYLOR?
WHO'S HE?
HE'S THE MAN GOD USED TO OPEN UP CHINA!
Accuel

HUDSON TAYLOR SET UP MEDICAL AND MISSIONARY STATIONS IN CHINA . . . HE EVEN DRESSED LIKE THE CHINESE, TO WIN THEM TO CHRIST.
. . . HE WATCHED BLOODY EXECUTIONS . . . HE WAS GOD'S MAN OF THE HOUR . . . AND HE COULD COOK A SIX COURSE MEAL FOR HIS FAMILY!
OK . . . OK! . . . I GOT THE MESSAGE!

MARK, THAT SMELLS DELICIOUS!
UMMM . . . HOW MUCH LONGER?
FRANK, WOULD YOU KINDLY GO CUT A FLOWER OUT IN THE GARDEN AND PUT IT IN THIS GLASS?
SOUNDS CRAZY . . . BUT I'LL DO IT!

SANDY, COULD YOU PLACE THE PILLOWS BEHIND YOUR MOTHER'S BACK SO SHE CAN SIT UP? . . . MAKE SURE SHE HAS A HEATING PAD, OK?
YES, MARK!
BILLY, IS THE TABLE SET?
ALL SET, MARK!

HERE'S THE FLOWER!
WOULD YOU PLEASE PUT IT ON THE TRAY, FRANK?
THE BIBLE SAYS . . . "AND THOUGH I BESTOW ALL MY GOODS TO FEED THE POOR,
AND THOUGH I GIVE MY BODY TO BE BURNED, AND HAVE NOT LOVE, IT PROFITETH ME NOTHING.—LOVE SUFFERETH LONG, AND IS KIND; LOVE ENVIETH NOT; LOVE VAUNTETH NOT ITSELF, IS NOT PUFFED UP" . . . 1 COR. 13:3, 4 FRANK . . . DO *YOU* KNOW WHAT THAT MEANS?
NO! I DON'T UNDERSTAND!

NOW WHEN YOU GIVE HELEN HER DINNER ON THIS TRAY . . . THIS LITTLE ACT OF KIND-NESS WILL MEAN NOTHING, IF YOU DON'T REALLY LOVE HER!
BUT I *DO* LOVE HER!
THEN WHEN YOU HAND IT TO HER, PLEASE TELL HER THAT YOU LOVE HER!

HI, HELEN . . . HERE'S DINNER! . . . . I . . . I LOVE YOU, HELEN!
(GASP!) . . . FRANK . . . I'M SPEECHLESS!

OHHH, FRANK IS SUCH A WONDERFUL MAN! . . . I REALLY LOVE HIM!

CHAPTER THREE

THE UGLY TRUTH!

BRAD, WHEN I ASK THE BLESSING YOU SHUT YOUR EYES LIKE THE REST OF US DO!
WELL I DON'T WANT TO BE A HYPOCRITE!
NOW, BRAD . . . YOU OBEY YOUR FATHER!
WHY?

THAT KID NEEDS A GOOD BEATING!
OVER MY DEAD BODY, FRANK MILLER!
YOU TELL HIM, MOM!
BESIDES, HE'S TOO OLD TO SPANK! . . . YOU'VE GOT TO REASON WITH BRAD! . . . DO YOU WANT TO GIVE HIM A COMPLEX?

ANYTHING ELSE YOU WANT TO SAY TO ME?
I'VE *NOTHING* MORE TO SAY TO YOU!
COME ON, BRAD . . . WE'LL BE LATE FOR SCHOOL!
GOODBYE, KIDS! HAVE A NICE DAY!

FRANK . . . I DON'T LIKE YOU PICKING ON BRAD ALL THE TIME!
I'M NOT GOING TO BE LATE ARGUING WITH YOU! . . . GOODBYE, HELEN!
WELL! . . . DON'T I EVEN GET A KISS?

EXCUSE ME, HELEN . . . BUT WHAT'S THE PROBLEM WITH BRAD AND HIS FATHER?
THERE'S NO PROBLEM! . . . YOU MUST REALIZE THERE'S A GENERATION GAP . . . BRAD WILL GROW OUT OF IT!
I'VE GOT TO GO, MARK . . . I'VE GOT TO BE AT CHURCH ALL DAY! . . . THE WOMEN'S MISSIONARY LEAGUE IS SEWING QUILTS FOR THE POOR!

LORD . . . SOMEHOW USE ME TO PULL FRANK AND LITTLE BRAD TOGETHER!

LATER THAT DAY

IS MRS. MILLER HOME?

NO, SHE'S AT CHURCH . . .
IS THERE A PROBLEM?

YES, SIR. WE MADE A DRUG RAID . . .
AND UNCOVERED 50 POUNDS OF
MARIJUANA . . . WE FOUND BRAD
VISITING THE PUSHERS . . .

INSTEAD OF TAKING HIM TO
JUVENILE HALL, WE BROUGHT
HIM HOME!

PLEASE COME IN, GENTLEMEN!

I'M A COUSIN VISITING THE FAMILY. WHAT CAN I DO TO HELP?
I DIDN'T KNOW THESE GUYS WERE USING DRUGS
THIS IS THE FOURTH TIME BRAD HAS BEEN AROUND KNOWN DRUG PUSHERS . . .
BUT THIS TIME WE CAUGHT HIM SMOKING MARIJUANA WITH THE OTHERS . . . BECAUSE OF HIS AGE WE BROUGHT HIM HOME SO HIS PARENTS CAN STRAIGHTEN HIM OUT . . .
IF NOT, HE'S GOING TO JUVENILE HALL!
GULP!

THANK YOU, GENTLEMEN . . . YOU'RE DOING A GREAT SERVICE!
THANK *YOU*, SIR! . . CALL US IF WE CAN BE OF FURTHER HELP!
LOUSEY ✶!!❋+#!! PIGS!

SIT DOWN, BRAD . . . I WANT TO TALK WITH YOU!
HEY . . . ARE YOU GONNA GET ON *MY* CASE NOW?
NO, BRAD, I LOVE YOU . . . AND I'VE BEEN PRAYING FOR YOU ALL DAY!
THERE'S SOMETHING I'D LIKE TO KNOW . . . ARE YOU A CHRISTIAN, BRAD? AND IF SO, WHEN WERE YOU SAVED!
YEAH, I'M A CHRISTIAN . . . I WAS SAVED LAST YEAR

BRAD, THE REASON ALL OF US GET INTO TROUBLE IS BECAUSE WE IGNORE GOD'S INSTRUCTIONS TO US IN THE BIBLE.
HAVE YOU EVER BEEN IN TROUBLE, MARK?
YES, BRAD, MANY TIMES!

BRAD, ONE OF GOD'S COMMANDMENTS IS TO HONOR YOUR FATHER AND MOTHER. EPH. 6:1
HONOR YOUR *FATHER*? HOW *CAN* I? WHEN HE EARNS MY RESPECT . . . *THEN* I'LL HONOR HIM!
BRAD, GOD MAKES NO DEALS! .. I DON'T CARE WHAT KIND OF PARENTS THEY'VE BEEN . . . GOD COMMANDS YOU TO DO IT!
YOU BELIEVE IN THE BIBLE DON'T YOU?
YES!

*For we must all appear before the judgment seat of Christ; that every one may receive the things done in his body, according to that he hath done, whether it be good or bad.

IT'S CALLED THE JUDGMENT SEAT OF CHRIST . . . IT WILL BE A JUDGMENT TIME FOR CHRISTIANS ONLY!
THIS IS WHEN WE GET OUR REWARDS FOR OUR FAITHFULNESS TO HIM.
MOST CHRISTIANS *DON'T* WANT TO HEAR ABOUT IT, BRAD . . . THEY *DON'T* WANT TO EVEN FACE IT . . . IF THEY DID, THEIR LIVES WOULD BE DIFFERENT.
WE WILL HAVE A LOT TO GIVE AN ACCOUNT FOR . . . I THINK WE'LL SHUDDER TO SEE WHAT WE *COULD* HAVE DONE FOR CHRIST.
BUT WE'RE TOO SELFISH OR TOO BUSY PLAYING CHURCH TO REALLY WORSHIP HIM!

*For other foundation can no man lay than that is laid, which is Jesus Christ. Now if any man build upon this foundation gold, silver, precious stones, wood, hay, stubble; Every man's work shall be made manifest: for the day shall declare it, because it shall be revealed by fire; and the fire shall try every man's work of what sort it is. If any man's work abide which he hath built thereupon, he shall receive a reward. If any man's work shall be burned, he shall suffer loss: but he himself shall be saved; yet so as by fire.

I Cor. 3:11-15

YOU TALK TO MY **DAD** ABOUT THIS . . . **NOT ME!** . . .
LET ME TELL YOU ABOUT *HIS* INFLUENCE!

ABOUT SIX MONTHS AGO, WE RODE OUR BIKES OVER TO A LIQUOR STORE TO GET SOME COKES . . . MY OLD MAN WAS IN THERE BUYING VODKA AND READING PLAYBOY! . . . THAT GOOD CHURCH GOER IS A BIG FAT PHONEY!
DO YOU KNOW HE ACTUALLY BOUGHT IT?
I FOUND EMPTY BOTTLES IN THE TRASH BARREL, INSIDE PAPER BAGS!
BRAD, LET'S TALK WITH YOUR FATHER TONIGHT AND GET THIS ALL IN THE OPEN!

FRANK . . . BRAD AND I WANT TO TALK WITH YOU IN THE DEN . . . IT'S VERY IMPORTANT!
CAN'T IT WAIT? . . . THERE'S A GOOD MOVIE COMING ON T.V.!
NO, IT CAN'T, DAD!
I'LL JOIN YOU!
I'M SORRY, HELEN . . . THIS IS MAN TO MAN TALK AND FRANK IS THE HEAD OF THE HOUSE!
WELL! . . . I LIKE THAT!

FATHER . . . HELP US TO COME TOGETHER IN LOVE AND UNDERSTANDING AND *SOFTEN* OUR HARD HEARTS IN JESUS' NAME.
AMEN!
WHAT'S GOING ON???

DAD . . . I SMOKE MARIJUANA BECAUSE YOU DRINK VODKA!
WHAT??
HOW DID YOU FIND OUT? . . . I MEAN . . . YOU SMOKE WHAT?? . . . I . . I DON'T KNOW WHAT TO SAY!

UH, WELL, I'LL ADMIT I DO TAKE A DRINK OCCASIONALLY, JUST TO BE SOCIABLE ... YOU KNOW "ALL THINGS IN MODERATION" ... BESIDES THAT, I'M UNDER A LOT OF TENSION!
ME TOO, DAD! ... THAT'S WHY I SMOKE POT!
AT LEAST YOU TWO HAVE SOMETHING IN COMMON NOW!

GOOD NIGHT! . . . IF THE CHURCH FOUND OUT ABOUT THIS WE'D NEVER LIVE IT DOWN . . . DOES HELEN KNOW ABOUT IT?
NO, FRANK, JUST THE POLICE AND US . . . LET'S PUT EVERYTHING ON THE TABLE!
THIS IS VERY UPSETTING! I'LL ADMIT, I . . I SINNED . . . DON'T STARE AT ME LIKE THAT! . . . IS THERE SOMETHING ELSE?
YEAH, DAD, THERE *IS!* . . . **YOU'RE A DIRTY OLD MAN!** I'VE SEEN YOU LOOKING AT SANDY'S GIRLFRIENDS SUNBATHING IN THE BACK YARD ...
I SAW YOU STARING AT THEM THROUGH THE CURTAINS . . . HOW *CAN* I RESPECT YOU?

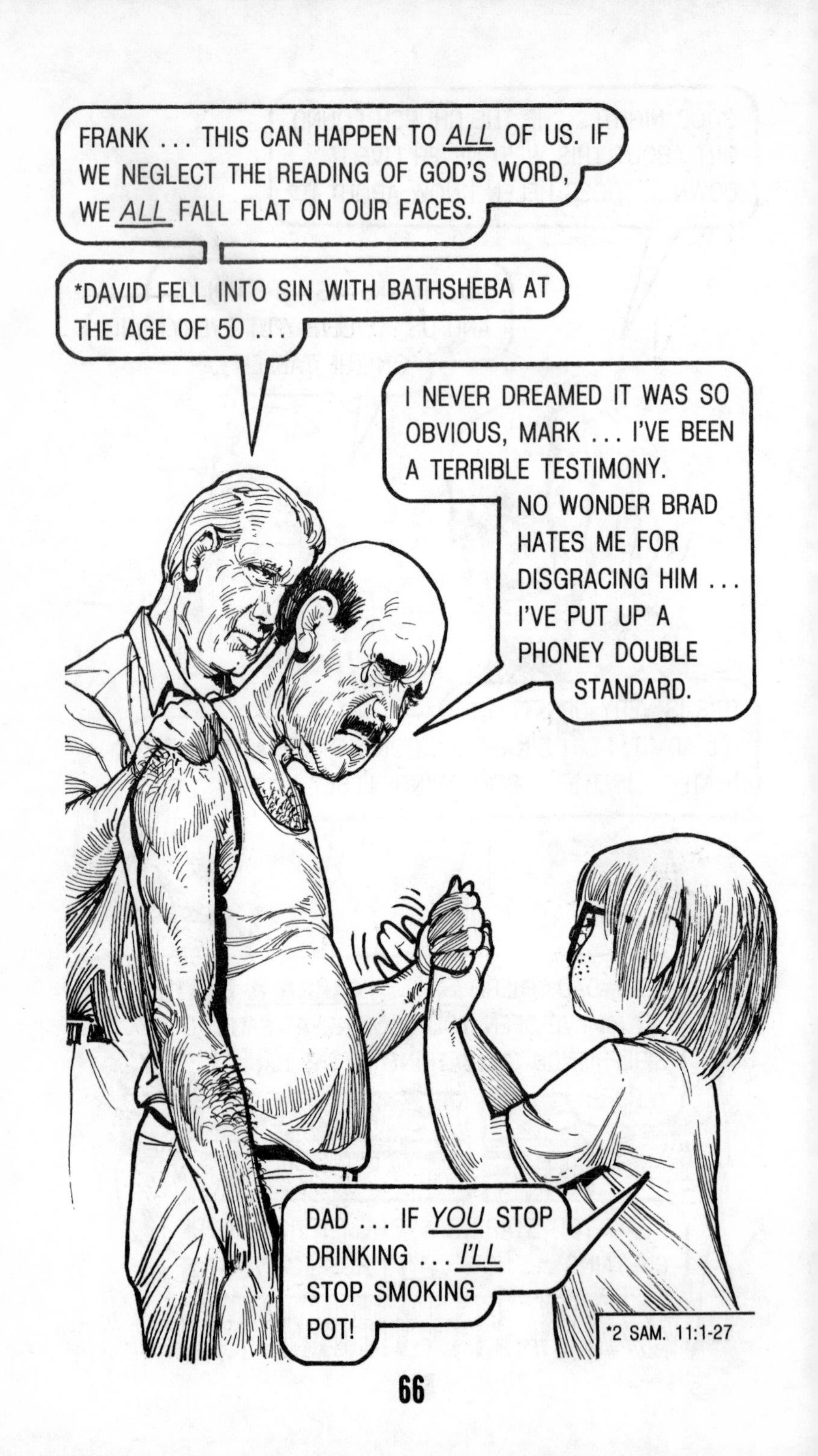
FRANK . . . THIS CAN HAPPEN TO ALL OF US. IF WE NEGLECT THE READING OF GOD'S WORD, WE ALL FALL FLAT ON OUR FACES.
*DAVID FELL INTO SIN WITH BATHSHEBA AT THE AGE OF 50 . . .
I NEVER DREAMED IT WAS SO OBVIOUS, MARK . . . I'VE BEEN A TERRIBLE TESTIMONY. NO WONDER BRAD HATES ME FOR DISGRACING HIM . . . I'VE PUT UP A PHONEY DOUBLE STANDARD.
DAD . . . IF YOU STOP DRINKING . . . I'LL STOP SMOKING POT!
*2 SAM. 11:1-27

BRAD. . . .SON, I'M SORRY, *PLEASE* FORGIVE ME FOR BEING A FLOP AS A FATHER . . . I PROMISE TO DO BETTER . . . WILL YOU GIVE ME A CHANCE, BRAD?

I FORGIVE YOU, DAD . . . (SNIF) AND I *DO* LOVE YOU . . . WILL *YOU* FORGIVE ME?

SOB

YES, BRAD!

And be ye kind one to another, tenderhearted, forgiving one another, even as God for Christ's sake hath forgiven you. EPH. 4:32

CHAPTER FOUR

MURDER?

HI, MOM . . . I BROUGHT YOU A CUP OF COFFEE!
WHY, SANDY . . . THANK YOU, DEAR!

I'D LIKE TO TALK TO YOU, MOM!
GO AHEAD, DEAR!

I'M PREGNANT!
OHH, MY GOD!
NOOOO!
CRASH!

MARK!! I NEED YOU!

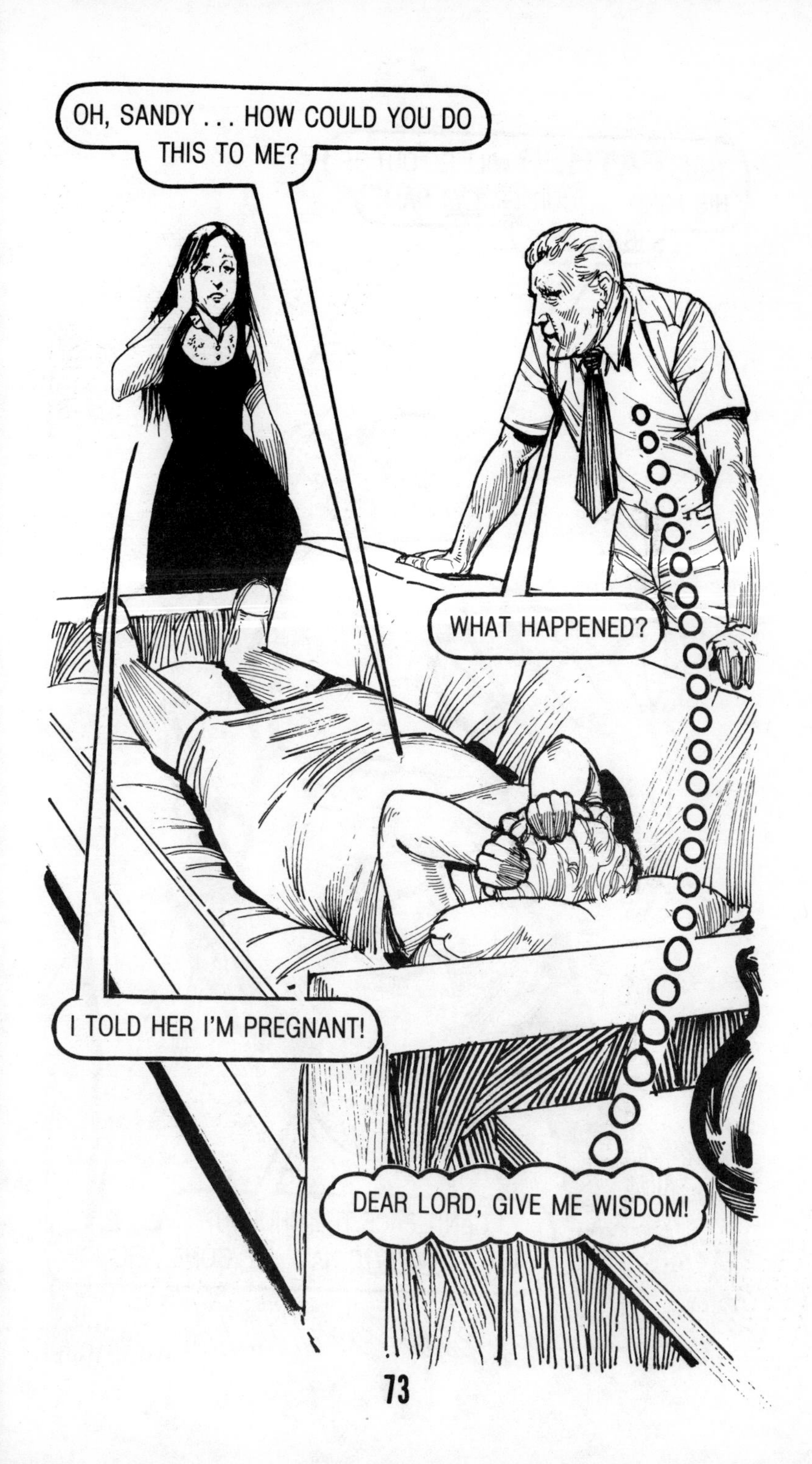
OH, SANDY . . . HOW COULD YOU DO THIS TO ME?
WHAT HAPPENED?
I TOLD HER I'M PREGNANT!
DEAR LORD, GIVE ME WISDOM!

YOUR **FATHER** WILL GO OUT OF HIS MIND . . . OUR *GOOD* NAME IS RUINED!
. . .I CAN'T FACE THE CHURCH . . . OHH . . . *WHERE* HAVE WE GONE WRONG?

I'VE GOT TO CALL YOUR FATHER!
MOTHER . . . CAN'T IT WAIT?
NO! . . . HE SHOULD KNOW!
WELL, AT LEAST I'M GETTING SOME ATTENTION!

MEANWHILE DOWN AT THE OFFICE

MR. MILLER . . . I'M HAVING PROBLEMS WITH MY DAUGHTER . . . SHE'S SANDY'S AGE . . . IS SANDY REBELLIOUS?

NOT AT ALL . . . YOU SEE, WE RAISED HER THE *RIGHT* WAY!

NK MILLER

EXCUSE ME, RUTH . . . .
THE PHONE!
RING!

GOOD MORNING! . . . FRANK MILLER SPEAKING!
SANDY'S PREGNANT!
GASP!

UH . . . I . . . UH . . . I'LL BE GONE FOR THE REST OF THE DAY, RUTH!
YES, MR. MILLER!

SIGH . . . OH, HOW I ENVY THEM . . . THEIR HOME MUST BE LIKE *HEAVEN*!

WHERE'S THAT DIRTY LITTLE TRAMP? I SAID, WHERE IS SHE??
NOW FRANK, CALM DOWN! ... WE'RE INTELLIGENT ADULTS!

SHE'S IN THE DEN WITH MARK!
DOES *HE* KNOW ABOUT IT?
YES!
DON'T WE HAVE *ANY* PRIVACY ANYMORE?

I HAVE **ONE** QUESTION FOR YOU, YOUNG LADY! . . . **WHO'S** THE ANIMAL THAT GOT TO YOU? . . . **WHAT'S HIS NAME?**

I DON'T KNOW, DADDY!

YOU MEAN YOU WERE RAPED? . . . SANDY, *WHY* DIDN'T YOU TELL US? . . . WAS HE A STRANGER? . . . DID HE THREATEN YOU IF YOU *TOLD*?

I'LL KILL HIM!!

DADDY . . . IT WAS ONE OF THE BOYS AT CHURCH!
WHICH ONE?
THAT'S THE PROBLEM . . . I *DON'T* KNOW!
GASP!
A DEATHLY SILENCE SETTLES OVER THE ROOM.

I'M SORRY, MOM AND DAD . . . MARK HAS BEEN TALKING TO ME . . . I'VE ASKED GOD TO FORGIVE ME . . . AND I WANT YOU TO FORGIVE ME, TOO!
SOB!
I CAN'T! . . . @!!✱#✱ I'LL NEVER FORGIVE YOU FOR HUMILIATING YOUR MOTHER AND ME LIKE THIS!

EXCUSE ME FOR BUTTING IN, FRANK. WHAT WOULD IT BE LIKE IF CHRIST WOULDN'T FORGIVE US?
THAT'S GOT NOTHING TO DO WITH THIS!
I'M SORRY, FRANK, BUT IT HAS EVERYTHING TO DO WITH THIS . . . IF HE DIDN'T FORGIVE US, THEN WE'D ALL BE GOING TO THE LAKE OF FIRE . . . . FRANK, YOU HAVE TO FORGIVE SANDY!

DO YOU REMEMBER THIS SCRIPTURE, FRANK?

MATT. 18:21, 22

YEAH, YEAH . . . I REMEMBER!

2 HOURS LATER
WE'RE SORRY, SANDY . . . WE DO FORGIVE YOU!
WE'LL TRY TO WORK THIS OUT TOGETHER, SANDY!

I KNOW THIS IS A *VERY* DELICATE SITUATION, BUT I'M *ONLY* TRYING TO HELP . . . LET'S ASSUME THE BABY *IS* ON THE WAY . . . ARE YOU GOING TO KEEP IT, SANDY?
I . . . *DON'T* KNOW!
DON'T BE RIDICULOUS . . . OF *COURSE* SHE ISN'T!

I FEEL IT SHOULD BE HANDLED *THIS* WAY! . . . FIRST OF ALL WE HAVE TO KEEP THE WHOLE THING *HUSH HUSH!* . . . I KNOW A DOCTOR WHO CAN PERFORM AN ABORTION OVER IN VALEVIEW!
BUT, DADDY . . . WHY ABORTION?
BECAUSE THE SUPREME COURT HAS MADE IT LEGAL!

ISAIAH 49:1, PSALMS 139:13-16

I'D LIKE TO READ A LITTLE STORY TO YOU!
DEC. 16th—TODAY MY LIFE BEGAN. MY PARENTS DO NOT KNOW IT YET. I AM AS SMALL AS A SEED OF AN APPLE, BUT IT IS I ALREADY. AND I AM TO BE A GIRL. I SHALL HAVE BLOND HAIR AND AZURE EYES. JUST ABOUT EVERYTHING IS SETTLED THOUGH, EVEN THE FACT THAT I SHALL LOVE FLOWERS.
DEC. 21st—SOME SAY THAT I AM NOT A REAL PERSON YET, THAT ONLY MY MOTHER EXISTS. BUT I AM A REAL PERSON JUST AS A SMALL CRUMB OF BREAD IS YET TRULY BREAD. MY MOTHER IS, AND I AM.

DEC. 28th—MY HEART BEGAN TO BEAT TODAY ALL BY ITSELF. FROM NOW ON IT SHALL GENTLY BEAT FOR THE REST OF MY LIFE WITHOUT EVER STOPPING TO REST! . . . AND AFTER MANY YEARS IT WILL TIRE. IT WILL STOP, AND THEN I SHALL DIE.

JAN. 7th—I AM GROWING A BIT EVERY DAY. MY ARMS AND LEGS ARE BEGINNING TO TAKE SHAPE. BUT I HAVE TO WAIT A LONG TIME YET BEFORE THOSE LITTLE LEGS WILL RAISE ME TO MY MOTHER'S ARMS, BEFORE THESE LITTLE ARMS WILL BE ABLE TO GATHER FLOWERS AND EMBRACE MY FATHER!

JAN. 16th — TINY FINGERS ARE BEGINNING TO FORM ON MY HANDS. FUNNY HOW SMALL THEY ARE! I SHALL BE ABLE TO STROKE MY MOTHER'S HAIR WITH THEM, AND I SHALL TAKE HER HAIR TO MY MOUTH AND SHE WILL PROBABLY SAY "OH, NO, NO, DEAR"...

JAN. 21st — IT WASN'T UNTIL TODAY THAT THE DOCTOR TOLD MOM THAT I AM LIVING HERE UNDER HER HEART. OH, MOM, HOW HAPPY SHE MUST BE! ARE YOU HAPPY, MOM?

JAN. 25th — MY MOM AND DAD ARE PROBABLY THINKING ABOUT A NAME FOR ME. BUT THEY DON'T EVEN KNOW THAT I'M A GIRL. THEY ARE PROBABLY SAYING ANDY. BUT I WANT TO BE CALLED CATHY. I AM GETTING SO BIG ALREADY!

FEB. 24th — I WONDER IF MOM HEARS THE WHISPER OF MY HEART? . . . SOME CHILDREN COME INTO THE WORLD A LITTLE SICK. AND THEN THE DELICATE HANDS OF THE DOCTOR PERFORM MIRACLES TO BRING THEM TO HEALTH.

IT BEATS SO EVENLY . . . TUP . . TUP . . TUP . . . YOU'LL HAVE A HEALTHY LITTLE DAUGHTER, MOM!

TIME TABLE FOR MURDER — PRINTED WITH THE PERMISSION OF THE REMNANT VOL. 3 NO. 10 2539 MORRISON AVE., ST. PAUL, MINN. 35117.

THAT SETTLES IT! . . . IF I CAN'T KEEP THE BABY . . . THEN IT WILL GO TO A CHRISTIAN HOME FOR ADOPTION.
WHY DON'T WE PRAY ABOUT IT TONIGHT AND TALK IT OVER TOMORROW?

NEXT MORNING
MAMA! . . . I'VE GOT GREAT NEWS! . . . GUESS WHAT?
IT WAS A FALSE ALARM!
(GASP) . . . THANK YOU, DEAR LORD . . . THANK YOU!

CHAPTER FIVE

UNTIL DEATH US DO PART

NOTE:

THIS CHAPTER DEALS WITH DIVORCE . . . SOME FAMILIES ARE SO MESSED UP AND ENTANGLED THAT ONLY GOD ALONE CAN SOLVE THE PROBLEM.

OH, **NO!** . . . HERE COMES BILLY AND THAT *THING* HE WANTS TO MARRY . . .
. . . AND HER *NO-GOOD* SISTER AND HER BRAT IS WITH THEM!

WHERE ARE YOU GOING, HELEN?
I'M GOING FOR A WALK . . . I CAN'T *STAND* THAT GIRL . . . GOODBYE!
HEY! . . . ANYBODY HOME?

MARK, . . . I WANT YOU TO MEET MY FIANCÉE, GLORIA, AND HER SISTER, PAT! . . . AND THIS LITTLE MONSTER IS STEVIE, JR.
MY PLEASURE!

WHEN'S THE HAPPY WEDDING DAY?
NEXT MONTH ON THE 17th!
OH, I'M SORRY . . . I'LL BE GONE BY THEN . . . I'LL HAVE TO MISS IT!
WELL AT LEAST YOU CAN SEND US A GIFT!
OF COURSE, I WILL!

ARE YOU A CHRISTIAN, GLORIA?
SURE . . . I'VE ALWAYS GONE TO CHURCH!
I DIDN'T ASK YOU ABOUT CHURCH . . . HAVE YOU BEEN *BORN AGAIN?
OH, YEAH, AT CAMP. I WAS ONLY NINE YEARS OLD!
*JOHN 3:3, 5, 7

MARK, WHEN WE GET MARRIED . . . WE'RE GONNA MOVE IN WITH MY FOLKS TO SAVE MONEY . . . WON'T *THAT* BE GREAT?
FORGIVE ME FOR SAYING THIS, BILLY . . . BUT IT WILL BE A NIGHTMARE!
ARE YOU SAYING WE SHOULD SHACK UP?
NO! GLORIA!

BILLY . . . YOU ARE YOUR MOTHER'S PRIDE AND JOY . . . SHE CARRIED YOU FOR NINE MONTHS . . . SHE TOOK CARE OF YOU WHEN YOU WERE SICK . . . SHE WORRIED ABOUT YOU, FED AND CLOTHED YOU . . .
. . . AND NOW, SOME STRANGE WOMAN WHO SHE COULD REALLY GROW TO HATE, IS GOING TO TAKE YOU AWAY FROM HER!

DO YOU THINK MOM HATES GLORIA? . . . THAT'S *IMPOSSIBLE*, MARK . . . MOM LOVES HER . . . EVEN THOUGH GLORIA HAS A MIND OF HER OWN!
RIGHT! NOBODY IS GONNA PUSH *US* AROUND

GLORIA, SOME CHRISTIAN HOMES BECOME HELLS BECAUSE OF *PRIDE AND REBELLION . . . ONLY WHEN THE PEOPLE IN THAT HOME ARE FULLY YIELDED TO CHRIST, READ HIS WORD AND HAVE *HIS* LOVING SPIRIT IS THERE HAPPINESS!

WHAT KIND OF HOME WILL *YOU* HAVE?

NOW, BACK TO MOVING IN WITH YOUR PARENTS! . . . *YOU CAN'T!* . . . IT'S UNSCRIPTURAL!

AHHH, COME ON, MARK . . . PROVE IT!

*Pride goeth before destruction, and an haughty spirit before a fall. Prov. 16:18

THE BIBLE SAYS IN GEN. 2:24 . . . EPH. 5:31 THAT YOU ARE TO LEAVE YOUR MOM AND DAD AND CLING OR HOLD FAST TO YOUR WIFE, AND THEN YOU AND GLORIA ARE TO BECOME ONE FLESH!
BUT WHERE DO WE GO?
IF YOU HAVE A JOB, THEN RENT A LITTLE PLACE AND START YOUR HOME . . . AWAY FROM RELATIVES! BUT IF YOU DON'T HAVE A JOB . . . WAIT UNTIL YOU CAN SUPPORT A WIFE!

BOY . . . I WISH YOU'D TALK TO THAT IDIOT I'M MARRIED TO! . . . HE WANTS ME TO WORK SO HE CAN TAKE IT EASY . . .
I CAN'T STOMACH HIM MUCH LONGER!
PATTY. . .WHAT ABOUT YOUR HOME?. . . ARE YOU SAVED?
OF COURSE, I'M SAVED . . . WE'RE MEMBERS OF BILLY'S CHURCH!

STEVIE, **STOP THAT!!** — OHH, THAT KID DRIVES ME UP THE WALL . . . HE'S *JUST* LIKE HIS FATHER!
UNGH!

OH, GOD, I WISH I'D NEVER HAD HIM! . . . MY MOTHER SAYS HE'S THE *UGLIEST* KID SHE'S EVER SEEN . . . SHE'S RIGHT!
HE LOOKS JUST LIKE STEVE!
PAT . . . THE BIBLE SAYS . . .*"CHILDREN ARE AN HERITAGE OF THE LORD AND THE FRUIT OF THE WOMB IS HIS REWARD!"
*PSALM 127:3

*"ALL THINGS WERE MADE BY HIM (JESUS); AND WITHOUT HIM WAS NOT ANYTHING MADE THAT WAS MADE." JOHN 1:3
**". . . AND THE GOD (JESUS) IN WHOSE HAND THY BREATH IS." DANIEL 5:23
***"AND THESE WORDS, WHICH I COMMAND THEE THIS DAY, SHALL BE IN THINE HEART: AND THOU SHALT TEACH THEM DILIGENTLY UNTO THY CHILDREN." DEUT. 6:6, 7

PAT, HAVEN'T ANY OF THE OLDER LADIES IN YOUR CHURCH EVER TALKED TO YOU ABOUT LOVING YOUR HUSBAND AND CHILD?
NO, ARE THEY SUPPOSED TO?
HELEN, I'M GLAD YOU'RE BACK. WILL YOU COME IN HERE, PLEASE?
GOOD GRIEF, THEY'RE STILL HERE!

OH, HELLO EVERYBODY .. IT'S SO NICE TO SEE YOU!
HELEN, MAY I ASK YOU, DID YOU EVER TELL PAT TO LOVE HER HUSBAND AND SON?
OF COURSE NOT! . . . IT'S NONE OF MY BUSINESS!
I'M AFRAID IT IS, HELEN!

THIS IS ONE OF THE REASONS THE CHURCH IS WEAK! —HELEN, IF YOU HAD READ YOUR BIBLE YOU WOULD HAVE UNDERSTOOD THAT IT IS YOUR RESPONSIBILITY!
I NEVER HEARD OF SUCH A THING!
HELEN, YOU'LL FIND THAT IN TITUS, CHAPTER 2:4, 5 THAT THE OLDER LADIES ARE TO TEACH THE YOUNGER ONES TO LOVE THEIR HUSBANDS AND THEIR CHILDREN!
I WISH SOMEONE HAD HELPED ME LIKE THAT WHEN I WAS FIRST MARRIED. IT WOULD HAVE MADE THINGS MUCH EASIER! . . . EVERYBODY SAID I WAS TOO GOOD FOR HIM . . . I COULD HAVE DONE SO MUCH BETTER!

OH, JUST FORGET ABOUT IT! . . . OUR MARRIAGE IS JUST ONE BIG DISASTER! . . . I THINK I'LL GET A LAWYER NEXT WEEK AND FILE FOR DIVORCE . . . STEVE IS SUCH A JERK . . . . ANYWAY I CAN ALWAYS REMARRY!
PAT, IS STEVE REALLY AS BAD AS YOU PICTURE HIM? . . . ISN'T HE UNDER PRESSURE TOO?

WELL, YEAH, . . . I GUESS HE IS! . . . HE'S HOLDING DOWN TWO JOBS . . . BUT YOU KNOW, MARK . . . IT'S JUST A LOT OF LITTLE THINGS THAT ALL PILE UP TOGETHER!
IT'S JUST ONE BIG MESS! . . . I CAN'T TAKE IT ANYMORE! . . . DIVORCE IS THE ONLY ANSWER!
Read . . . DIVORCE & REMARRIAGE by Guy Duty, Bethany Fellowship, Inc.

*And I say unto you, whosoever shall put away his wife, except it be for fornication, and shall marry another, committeth adultery; and whoso marrieth her which is put away doth commit adultery. Matt. 19:9

SATAN ATTACKS THE CHRISTIAN HOMES BY APPEALING TO OUR WEAKNESSES . . . WHEN YOUR FEELINGS ARE HURT, THAT'S PRIDE!
SO YOU *WANT* TO GET EVEN . . . IT STARTS WITH LITTLE INSINUATIONS, THEN INSULTS WHICH TRIGGER OFF ARGUMENTS . . .
THEN FIGHTS TURN THE HOME INTO A LIVING HELL!
WOW . . . DOES *THAT* SOUND FAMILIAR!

AND INSTEAD OF FORGIVING AND LOVING, OR TRYING TO UNDERSTAND THE OTHER PERSON'S PROBLEMS,
WE SELFISHLY HURT WITH ANOTHER UNKIND AND THOUGHTLESS COMMENT, AND THE WAR IS ON!
THAT'S THE WAY STEVE AND I ARE!
IT'S LIKE THIS ALL OVER THE WORLD, PAT!

THEN THE BATTLE BEGINS TO RAGE IN THE MIND . . . THEY BECOME SO MISERABLE THAT THEY START THINKING . . .

ABOUT HOW NICE IT WOULD BE IF THEY WERE MARRIED TO THAT PERSON LIVING DOWN THE STREET . . .

WHICH WILL LEAD THEM TO DISASTER!

OH, MY GOD . . . HE KNOWS ALL ABOUT ME!

YOU SEE, PAT, THE BIBLE SAYS "THOU WILT KEEP HIM IN PERFECT PEACE, WHOSE MIND IS STAYED ON THEE:" ISAIAH 26:3
LOOK, PAT, EVEN IF YOU BELIEVE YOU ARE RIGHT . . . GO THE EXTRA MILE AND ASK YOUR HUSBAND TO FORGIVE YOU . . . GIVE 150% IF HE ONLY GIVES 50% . . . IF YOU ARE INSULTED, THEN TRY TO TAKE IT GRACIOUSLY . . .
I KNOW IT'S HARD BUT GOD WILL HELP YOU. YOU SEE, LOVE IS LONG SUFFERING 1 COR. 13th CHAPTER

ANGELS ARE WATCHING . . SO IS THE LORD. LEARN TO BITE YOUR TONGUE . . . BE CONTENT . . . BE PATIENT . . . BE GRATEFUL FOR WHAT YOU HAVE!

STOP CRITICIZING . . . THANK GOD FOR YOUR MATE, IT *COULD* BE MUCH WORSE . . . NOBODY IS PERFECT, ONLY CHRIST IS PERFECT!

PAT, *DIVORCE IS A COP-OUT!*

IF YOU BELIEVE GOD'S WORD, WHERE HUSBANDS SHOULD LOVE THEIR WIVES EVEN AS CHRIST ALSO LOVED THE CHURCH, AND GAVE HIMSELF FOR IT (EPH. 5:25)

AND YOU SUBMIT, AS INSTRUCTED IN EPHESIANS 5:22-24 . . . IF YOU REALLY DID THAT . . . SATAN WOULD BE STOPPED COLD!

WHEN YOU TALK DIVORCE, YOU HELP DESTROY YOUR LITTLE SON. CHRISTIANS ARE SELFISH, INCONSIDERATE AND COMPLETELY WALKING IN THE FLESH WHEN A CHRISTIAN HOME IS DESTROYED!
IT'S NOT GOD'S FAULT — IT'LL BE BECAUSE THEY DIDN'T TRUST HIM OR KEEP THEIR EYES ON HIM!
WHY DID HE GO TO THE CROSS? . . . AND SUFFER? . . . IT WAS TO SHOW YOU WHAT THE WORD, "LOVE," REALLY MEANS!

LET ME ASK *YOU* A QUESTION . . . WHAT IF YOUR WIFE CHEATED ON YOU WITH ANOTHER MAN . . . WOULD YOU DIVORCE HER?
NO, I WOULD FORGIVE HER!
WHAT IF SHE CHEATED WITH ANOTHER WOMAN?
I WOULD STILL FORGIVE HER . . . BECAUSE I LOVED HER, PAT!

*BUT AS THE DAYS OF NOAH WERE, SO SHALL ALSO THE COMING OF THE SON OF MAN BE. *MATT. 24:87*

IN THE DAYS OF *NOAH, THEY WERE MARRYING AND GIVING IN MARRIAGE AND THE FLOOD CAME AND CARRIED THEM AWAY . . . THEY LEFT GOD OUT OF THEIR LIVES! . . . TODAY WE ARE DOING THE SAME THING.
DO YOU THINK JESUS IS COMING SOON?
ABSOLUTELY . . . IT'S NOT TOO FAR AWAY . . . PROPHECY IS BEING FULFILLED RIGHT BEFORE OUR EYES . . . IT WON'T BE MUCH LONGER
*LUKE 17:27

MAYBE I'D BETTER STAY WITH STEVE AFTER ALL!
THAT'S WHAT GOD *EXPECTS* YOU TO DO, PAT!
ONE MORE THING, MARK ... UH ... YOU SEE STEVE REALLY ISN'T SAVED ... SO I WAS THINKING ...

I'M GOING TO *TALK* HIM INTO ACCEPTING CHRIST!
PAT, TOO MANY CHRISTIAN WOMEN HAVE BECOME WRECKS BECAUSE THEY TRIED TO PREACH TO THEIR UNSAVED HUSBANDS.
HOW WILL HE FIND CHRIST?

READ 1 PETER 3:1-6

*PAT . . . THE TWO OF YOU . . . THAT IS, JESUS AND YOU, CAN DO IT!
I THANK GOD I MET YOU . . . MARK! . . . NOW, I'LL BE A BETTER WIFE AND MOTHER!
*JOHN 14:23 1 CORIN. 3:9

PAT, DEAR, I'M SORRY I'VE NEVER SPOKEN TO YOU ABOUT MARRIAGE . . . IT WAS COMPLETE IGNORANCE ON MY PART . . . WILL YOU FORGIVE ME?
OF COURSE, MRS. MILLER. WE BOTH LEARNED A LOT TODAY!

UH, MARK . . . I'M SORRY FOR THE WAY I ACTED, I JUST PUT ON A BIG FRONT! . . . I'M REALLY A SCARED LITTLE MOUSE. BILLY AND I WILL HAVE OUR OWN LITTLE PLACE . . . THANK YOU FOR STRAIGHTENING US OUT!
I LOVE YOU AND BILLY . . . I'LL BE PRAYING THAT GOD WILL RICHLY BLESS YOUR UNION AND THAT CHRIST WILL BE THE HEAD OF YOUR HOME ... HE WILL IF YOU STAY IN THE SCRIPTURES.

CHAPTER SIX

THE GOOD SAMARITAN

YAAAAAAH!

WHAT'S WRONG?

DID YOU SEE WHAT THAT IDIOT IN THE WHITE HOUSE DID TODAY?
YOU MEAN THE LORD'S ANOINTED?

LORD'S ANOINTED? I'M NOT TALKING ABOUT KING DAVID . . . *I* MEAN THE PRESIDENT!

FRANK, KING *SAUL WAS THE LORD'S ANOINTED. SO WAS HITLER AND SO IS THE **PRESIDENT OR ANY OTHER WORLD LEADER.

*1 SAM. 24:6, 10 **DAN. 2:21

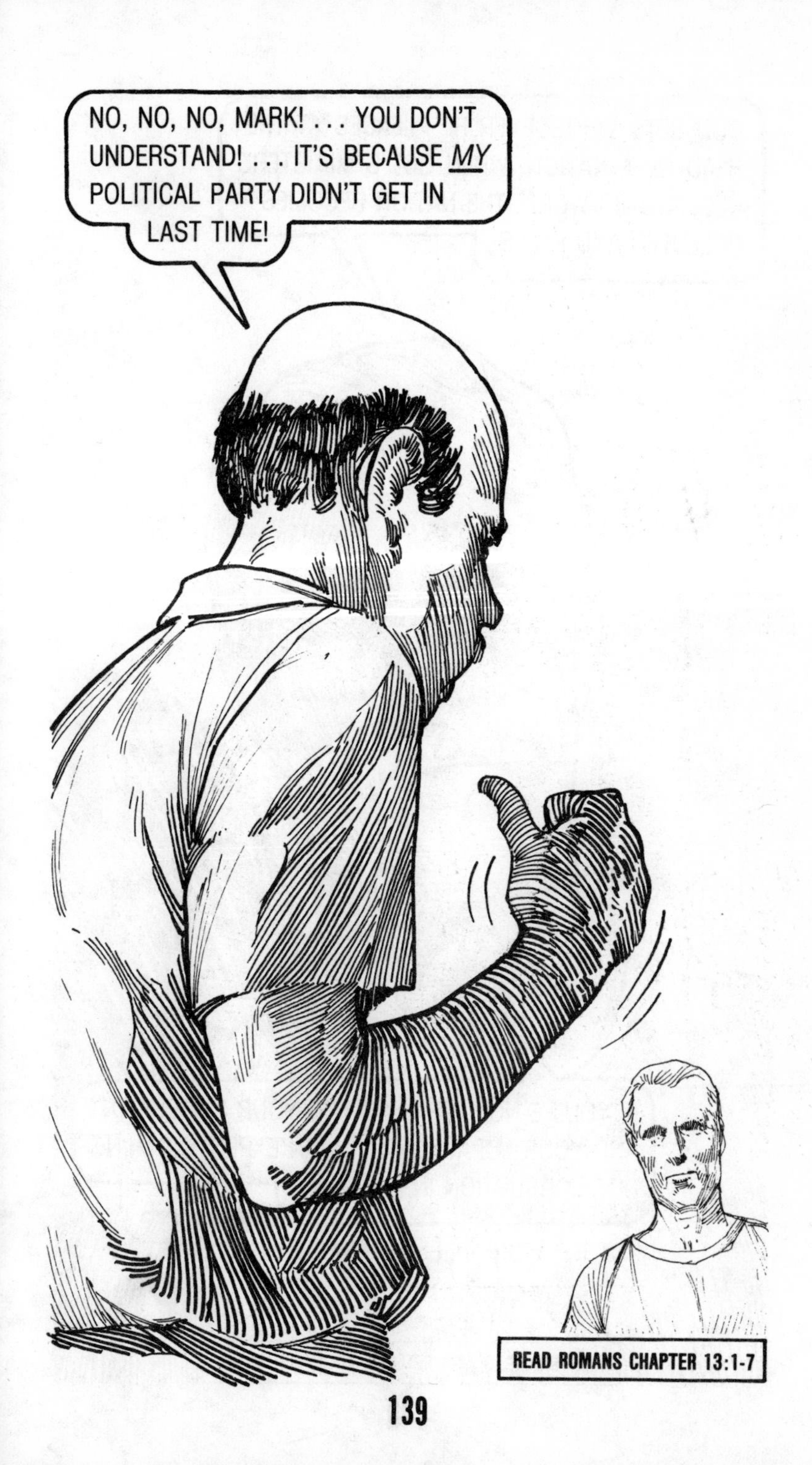
NO, NO, NO, MARK! . . . YOU DON'T UNDERSTAND! . . . IT'S BECAUSE *MY* POLITICAL PARTY DIDN'T GET IN LAST TIME!
READ ROMANS CHAPTER 13:1-7

GOD SETS WHOSOEVER HE PLEASES AT THE HEAD OF A NATION. WHEN GOD'S MINISTERS NEGLECT HIS WORD, THE NATION BECOMES POLLUTED AND FALLS.

IF YOU'RE NOT *PRAYING FOR YOUR **PRESIDENT AND YOUR ***PASTOR YOU CAN EXPECT NOTHING BUT CORRUPTION IN THE LAND.

*1 TIM. 2:2, 3 **1 PETER 2:17 ***EPH. 6:19

YOU ARE A *PILGRIM IN THIS WORLD AND YOU ARE JUST **PASSING THROUGH. WHEN YOU VOTE, PRAY ABOUT IT AND VOTE FOR THE MAN GOD LEADS YOU TO VOTE FOR.
CHRISTIANS SHOULD BE THE BEST CITIZENS THIS COUNTRY HAS . . . BECAUSE THEY'RE SUPPOSED TO BE HONEST IN *EVERY* PHASE OF THEIR LIVES, INCLUDING THE PAYING OF ***TAXES!
HE DIDN'T HAVE TO MENTION TAXES!
*1 PET. 2:11 **HEB. 11:13 ***2 CORIN. 8:21

HEY, MARK . . . WANT TO WALK WITH ME TO THE STORE?
CERTAINLY, BILLY!
BETTER PUT ON A COAT! . . . IT'S WINDY OUTSIDE!

HUMM . . . THAT'S SOME WIND!
HAW HAW HAW, LOOK! OLD MAN HARRIS IS GONNA LOSE HIS FRUIT TREE . . .
IT SERVES HIM RIGHT!
WE'D BETTER STAKE THE TREE FOR HIM! GO GET SOME ROPE, BILLY!

Whether therefore ye eat, or drink, or whatsoever ye do, do all to the glory of God. 1st CORIN. 10:31

WHAT ARE THEY DOING OUT THERE??
THEY'VE STAKED UP MY TREE! . . .
THAT'S THE FIRST KIND ACT ANYONE HAS EVER DONE FOR ME!

*Let your light so shine before men, that they may see your good works, and glorify your Father which is in heaven. MATT. 5:16

*For when we were with you, this we commanded you, that if any would not work, neither should he eat. 2nd THES. 3:10

OOH, OH! . . . HE MADE A MISTAKE!
DID THE CROOK SHORT-CHANGE YOU?
NO, HE OVERPAID ME!
HEY . . . ALL RIGHT! . . . KEEP IT . . . IT'S HIS LOSS!
THE LORD WOULDN'T LIKE THAT, BILLY!

YOU OVERPAID ME $5.00 . . . I'M RETURNING IT BECAUSE I'VE *GOT* TO GIVE AN ACCOUNT TO CHRIST FOR MY ACTIONS!
WOW, THANK YOU, SIR! THIS IS MY FIRST DAY HERE . . .
IF I'D COME UP SHORT, I COULD HAVE BEEN FIRED . . . YOU SURE SAVED MY NECK, CUZ I SURE NEED THIS JOB! . . . THANKS AGAIN, MISTER
(GULP) BOY, WHAT A LESSON!

MARK!...
LOOKOUT!

WAAAAH!
OH, MY GOD!
SCREECH!

MARK . . . ARE YOU ALRIGHT?
NO PROBLEM . . . IT ONLY GRAZED ME . . . AND I SLIPPED!
WAAAH!

MARK . . . YOU CAN SUE HER FOR EVERY DIME THEY HAVE! . . . LIE HERE 'TIL THE AMBULANCE COMES!
I CAN'T DO THAT, BILLY! . . . THAT WOULD BE DISHONEST!
BESIDES, . . ."ALL THINGS WORK TOGETHER FOR GOOD, TO THEM THAT LOVE GOD, TO THEM WHO ARE THE CALLED ACCORDING TO HIS PURPOSE." ROM. 8:28

EXCUSE ME, MISS . . . ARE YOU ALRIGHT?
SOB SOB
WAAAAAAAAHH!
I JUST RAN OVER SOMEBODY! . . . I LEFT MY DRIVER'S LICENSE AT HOME . . .
. . . MY BABY'S SICK . . . I'M LOST! . . . I CAN'T FIND THE HOSPITAL . . .
MY HUSBAND'S OUT OF WORK AND WE DON'T HAVE ANY MONEY . . . WHAT AM I GONNA DO?

DON'T CRY . . . EVERYTHING'S GOING TO BE ALRIGHT . . . YOU MISSED ME!
I JUST SLIPPED . . . COULD WE DRIVE YOU TO THE HOSPITAL?
OHH, THANK GOD . . UH . . . COULD YOU, PLEASE?

HERE, LET *ME* HOLD THE BABY FOR YOU!
HEY, I KNOW WHERE THE HOSPITAL IS, MARK!
WAAAAAH!

I BET IT'S GAS!
WE'RE ALMOST THERE!
PAT PAT
WE CAN'T AFFORD ANOTHER DOCTOR BILL!
LET'S PRAY ABOUT IT!

BURP!
GOO!
PRAISE THE LORD . . . THAT WAS IT!

I *REALLY* APPRECIATE ALL YOUR HELP . . . YOU WERE A GODSEND!
GOO!
THE LORD SET THIS UP FOR US . . . HERE'S A LITTLE TRACT I'D LIKE YOU TO READ . . .
AND A FEW DOLLARS TO HELP YOU AND YOUR HUBBY OUT . . . GOODBYE. MAY GOD BLESS YOU AND THAT BEAUTIFUL LITTLE BABY OF YOURS!
THIS IS *TOO* MUCH!

WHAT TOOK YOU TWO SO LONG? DID YOU GET LOST?
NO, HELEN, BUT WE HAD A WONDERFUL TIME . . . NEED SOME HELP?
WOW! . . . *THIS* GUY REALLY LIVES IT!

CHAPTER SEVEN

SHHHHHHH!

HONEY!
YEAH?

DON'T YOU WANT TO COME TO BED?
SHE'S GOT TO BE KIDDING!

YEAH, YEAH . . . I'LL COME TO BED AS SOON AS THIS IS OVER!
HUMMM
KISS ME, YOU FOOL!

LORD . . . PUT THE RIGHT WORDS IN MY MOUTH . . . THIS IS SUCH AN EXPLOSIVE AND DELICATE SUBJECT ...
OPEN THEIR HEARTS, LORD, SO THEIR MARRIAGE CAN BE HEALED.

FRANK . . . IS YOUR PROGRAM FINISHED?
YEAH . . . IT WAS PRETTY GOOD TONIGHT . . . WELL, I'LL SEE YOU IN THE MORNING, MARK . . . GOODNIGHT!
CLICK!
COULD I TALK WITH YOU FOR A FEW MINUTES, FRANK? . . . I THINK IT'S PRETTY IMPORTANT!

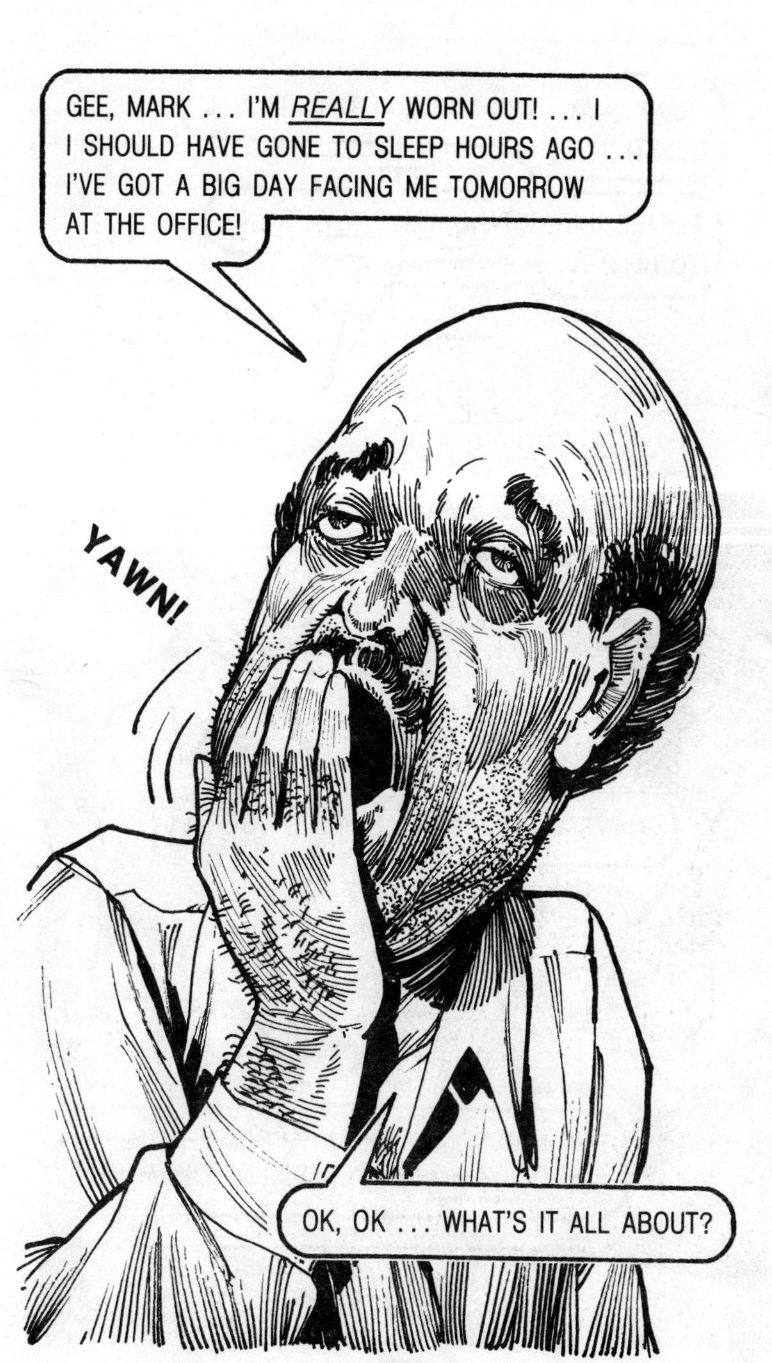
GEE, MARK ... I'M REALLY WORN OUT! ... I
I SHOULD HAVE GONE TO SLEEP HOURS AGO ...
I'VE GOT A BIG DAY FACING ME TOMORROW
AT THE OFFICE!
YAWN!
OK, OK ... WHAT'S IT ALL ABOUT?

FRANK, MAY I ASK YOU A VERY PERSONAL QUESTION? . . .
PLEASE UNDERSTAND, I'M *ONLY* TRYING TO HELP . . .
GO AHEAD . . . SHOOT!
THIS MAY SOUND LIKE A TV COMMERCIAL . . . BUT . . . *HOW'S* YOUR LOVE LIFE?

IT'S, UH . . . FANTASTIC!
COME ON, FRANK . . . LET'S HAVE THE TRUTH!
IT'S ROTTEN!

WHEN'S THE LAST TIME YOU MADE LOVE?
ABOUT A MONTH AND A HALF AGO!
THEN THERE'S TROUBLE IN RIVER CITY?
YEAH . . . I GUESS YOU CAN SAY THAT!

IN THE BIBLE THAT'S A *NO, NO*, FRANK! OUTSIDE OF ILLNESS . . . THE ONLY REASON FOR YOUR NOT MAKING LOVE IS BECAUSE OF PRAYER AND FASTING!
ARE *YOU* KIDDING?

NO, FRANK . . . IT SAYS IN 1st CORINTHIANS 7:5 "DEFRAUD YE NOT ONE THE OTHER, EXCEPT IT BE WITH CONSENT FOR A TIME, THAT YE MAY GIVE YOURSELVES TO FASTING AND PRAYER;
AND COME TOGETHER AGAIN, THAT SATAN TEMPT YOU NOT FOR YOUR INCONTINENCY". . . (THAT MEANS LACK OF SELF CONTROL)
YOU JUST WENT OVER MY HEAD, MARK . . . WHAT DOES SATAN HAVE TO DO WITH IT?

YOU'VE GOT 3 ENEMIES, FRANK . . . THE WORLD, THE LUST OF THE FLESH AND THE DEVIL. . .I JUST SAW ALL THREE OF THEM HIT YOU THROUGH THAT TV PROGRAM TONIGHT!
OHH . . . THAT'S CRAZY, MARK!
DIDN'T THAT BEAUTIFUL WOMAN TURN YOU ON WHEN SHE SAID . . . "KISS ME, YOU FOOL?"

WELL . . . A LITTLE, I GUESS. AFTER ALL I AM HUMAN!
HEY, FRANK . . . ALL OF US ARE HUMAN . . . AND THE DEVIL KNOWS OUR WEAK POINTS!
AND SEX CAN BE A WEAK SPOT!

I SEE . . . IF WE DO IT THE WAY THE BIBLE SAYS THEN I WON'T BE TEMPTED SO OFTEN
THAT'S RIGHT!

IF YOU ARE TEMPTED, FRANK . . . HERE ARE SOME GOOD THINGS TO READ IN THE SCRIPTURES!
PROVERBS
ESPECIALLY GOOD IS THE 39th CHAPTER OF GENESIS . . . THIS WILL SHOW YOU PITFALLS SATAN CAN SET UP . . .
ALSO PROVERBS, CHAPTERS 6, 7 AND 9

IN PROVERBS 5:15 IT SAYS . . . "DRINK WATERS OUT OF THINE *OWN* CISTERN, AND RUNNING WATERS OUT OF THINE OWN WELL". . .
WHAT DOES THAT MEAN?
IT MEANS, BE FAITHFUL AND TRUE TO YOUR *OWN* WIFE, FRANK!

FRANK . . . OUTSIDE OF THE LORD . . . WHO IS THE MOST IMPORTANT PERSON IN YOUR LIFE?
I GUESS IT'S MY WIFE!
THAT'S RIGHT!

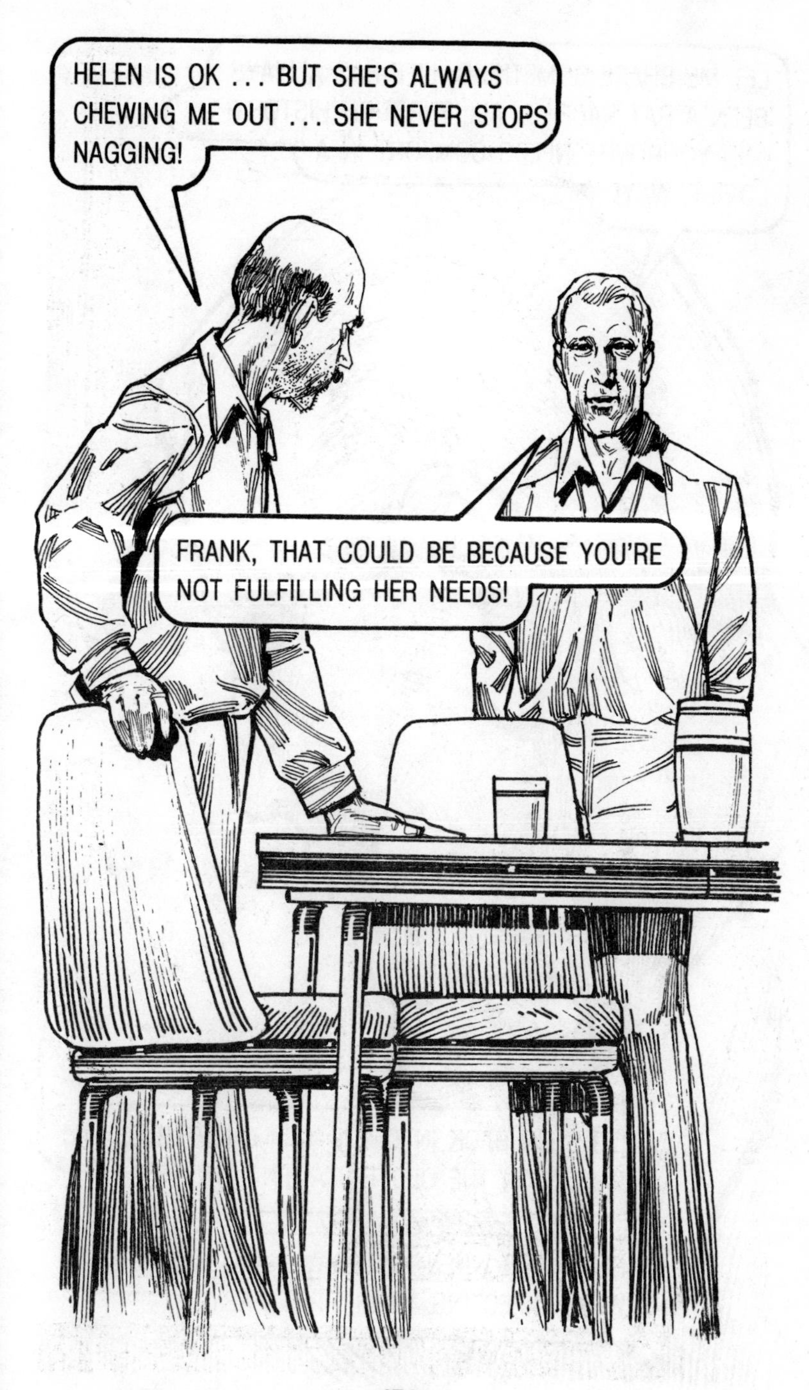
HELEN IS OK . . . BUT SHE'S ALWAYS CHEWING ME OUT . . . SHE NEVER STOPS NAGGING!
FRANK, THAT COULD BE BECAUSE YOU'RE NOT FULFILLING HER NEEDS!

LET ME SHARE SOMETHING. LIFE HAS ALWAYS BEEN A RAT RACE . . . ALL THROUGH HISTORY! . . . AND YOUR WIFE NEEDS COMFORT IN A LOVING WAY!
LET'S GO BACK INTO THE 12th CHAPTER OF 2nd SAMUEL IN THE OLD TESTAMENT . . .
REMEMBER WHEN KING DAVID AND BATHSHEBA WERE EXPECTING THEIR FIRST BABY?

YEAH . . . I THINK SO!
IT WAS A TIME OF GREAT SORROW AND THE LORD TOOK THE BABY HOME . . . IN OTHER WORDS, IT DIED!
AND THE BIBLE SAYS, "AND DAVID COMFORTED BATHSHEBA, HIS WIFE, AND WENT IN UNTO HER AND LAY WITH HER; AND SHE BORE A SON, AND HE CALLED HIS NAME SOLOMON, AND THE LORD LOVED HIM." 2nd SAM. 12:24

FRANK . . . DID YOU EVER NOTICE HOW NICE AND POLITE YOU AND HELEN TREAT EACH OTHER WHEN SOMEONE IMPORTANT COMES TO YOUR HOME?
YES!
IF YOU COULD CAPTURE THAT RESPECT ALL OF THE TIME, YOUR HOME WOULD BE PERFECT . . . AGAIN, THE *KEY IS IN THE SCRIPTURES.
*EPH. CHAPTER 5

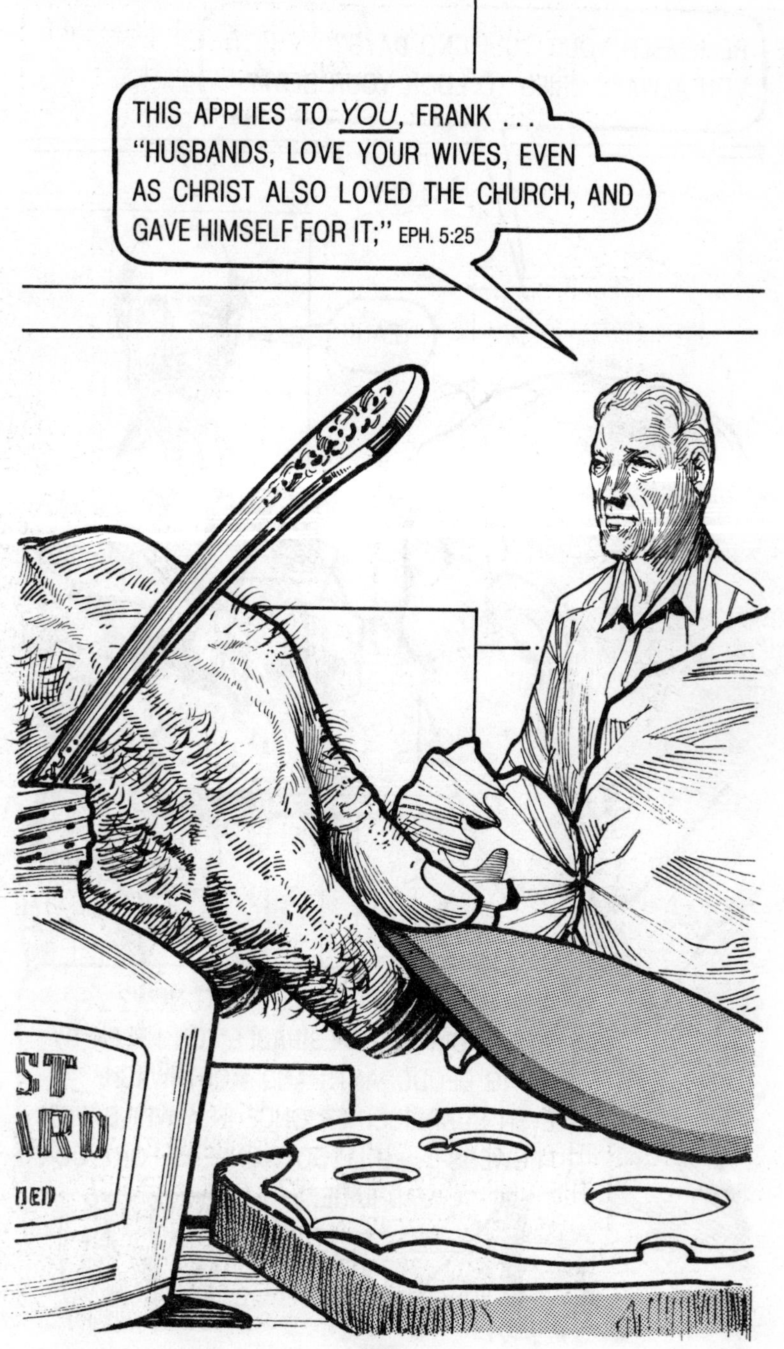
THIS APPLIES TO *YOU*, FRANK . . . "HUSBANDS, LOVE YOUR WIVES, EVEN AS CHRIST ALSO LOVED THE CHURCH, AND GAVE HIMSELF FOR IT;" EPH. 5:25

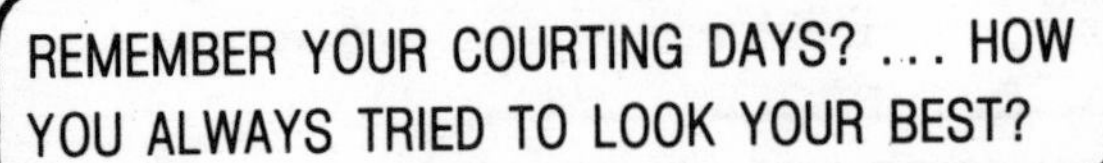

REMEMBER YOUR COURTING DAYS? .... HOW YOU ALWAYS TRIED TO LOOK YOUR BEST?
YEAH!
WHY NOT DO THE SAME THING NOW? ... MAKE YOURSELF DESIRABLE FOR HELEN BY USING DEODORANTS AND MOUTHWASH. EVEN SURPRISE HER ONCE IN A WHILE WITH FLOWERS ... IT'LL DO WONDERS FOR YOUR MARRIAGE!
GRAPE SODA

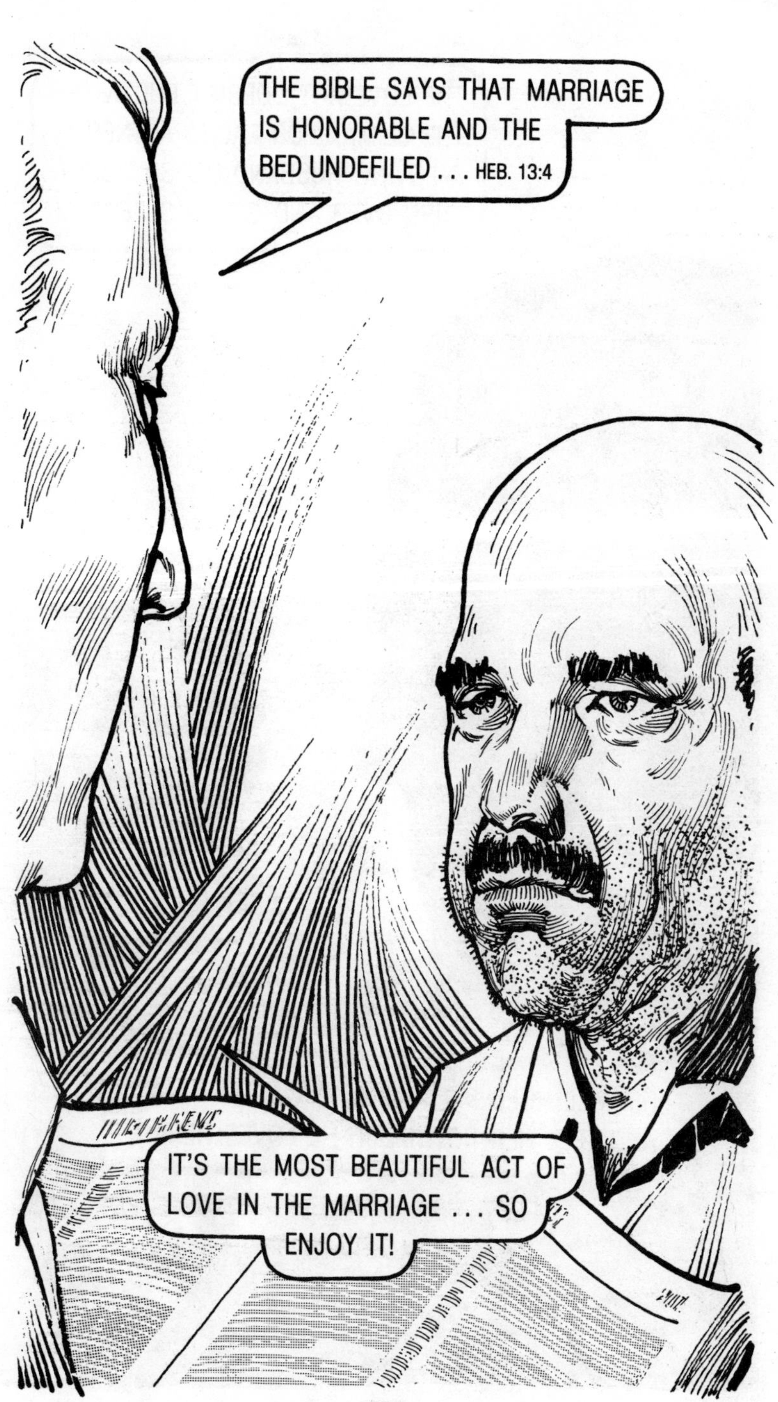
THE BIBLE SAYS THAT MARRIAGE IS HONORABLE AND THE BED UNDEFILED . . . HEB. 13:4
IT'S THE MOST BEAUTIFUL ACT OF LOVE IN THE MARRIAGE . . . SO ENJOY IT!

THE LOVE ACT DOESN'T END WITH THE CLIMAX FOR EACH PARTNER . . . A LOVING HUSBAND DOESN'T JUST TURN OVER AND GO TO SLEEP . . .
HE WILL HOLD HIS WIFE IN HIS ARMS AND TELL HER HOW MUCH HE LOVES HER!

I REALLY NEEDED THAT . . .
THANKS, MARK!
LET ME GIVE YOU JUST ONE OR TWO MORE GOODIES THAT WILL HELP YOU, FRANK.
OK, . . .
GO AHEAD!

FRANK, DON'T BE AFRAID TO SHOW YOUR AFFECTION FOR HELEN IN PUBLIC!
BURP! . . . AHH, THAT WAS GOOD!
HOLD HER HAND OR GIVE HER A KISS AND A SQUEEZE ONCE IN A WHILE . . . THAT'LL MAKE HER PROUD THAT HER HUSBAND LOVES HER THAT MUCH!
GEE, MARK . . . I'D FEEL LIKE A NUT!
TRY IT AND SEE IF SHE LIKES IT . . . . I BET SHE WILL!

DON'T EMBARRASS HELEN ABOUT HER WEIGHT . . . INSTEAD OF CRITICISING HER, COMPLIMENT HER . . . EVERYBODY NEEDS ENCOURAGEMENT. STOP PUTTING HER DOWN!
ONE LAST THING, FRANK . . . HUSBANDS WILL LISTEN TO EVERYBODY BUT THEIR OWN WIVES . . . *SHE IS YOUR BEST FRIEND SO PAY ATTENTION. DON'T TUNE HER OUT . . . SHE LOVES YOU!

*PROV. 5:18, 19

FRANK, I'D LIKE TO TALK TO HELEN ABOUT THIS, EXPLAINING IT THROUGH THE SCRIPTURES . . . THAT IS, IF I HAVE YOUR PERMISSION!
YOU BET, MARK! . . . ANYTHING TO HELP OUR MARRIAGE GROW!

HELEN . . . I TALKED TO FRANK ABOUT BEING A BETTER HUSBAND!
WELL, HE CERTAINLY NEEDS IT!

HE DIDN'T SEEM TO UNDERSTAND WHAT THE BIBLE HAS TO SAY ABOUT HUSBANDS MAKING LOVE TO THEIR WIVES!
HUMPH! . . . YOU CAN SAY THAT AGAIN!

I'VE TOLD FRANK TO MAKE HIMSELF AS ATTRACTIVE AS POSSIBLE BY SHAVING AND USING DEODORANTS, AND TO BE GENTLE AND LOVING.
WHY, HOW NICE!

HELEN, THE BIBLE HAS A LOT TO SAY ABOUT SEX BETWEEN THE HUSBAND AND WIFE AND HOW THE ACT CAN BECOME A THING OF BEAUTY!
AS FAR AS I'M CONCERNED . . . IT'S A NIGHTMARE AND I CAN DO WITHOUT IT!

THAT'S A SINFUL ATTITUDE, HELEN . . . BECAUSE IT'S PUTTING YOUR MARRIAGE IN JEOPARDY!
YOUR HUSBAND IS FACING HIS MIDDLE-AGE SYNDROME AND IF YOU AREN'T ON GUARD, IT COULD BE DISASTEROUS TO YOUR FAMILY!

WHAT'S A MIDDLE-AGE SYNDROME?
IT'S WHEN A MAN HITS MIDDLE AGE. HE FEELS HE'S GOING OVER THE HILL AND ALL AT ONCE ALL THE YOUNG LADIES START APPEALING TO HIM!
FRANK WOULD *NEVER* DO SUCH A THING! . . . HE LOVES ME!

*Wherefore let him that thinketh he standeth take heed lest he fall.

1 COR. 10:12

WHAT CAN BE DONE TO HOLD HIM?
FIRST OF ALL . . . GET INTO THE SCRIPTURES WITH HIM . . . THEN MAKE YOURSELF AS ATTRACTIVE AS POSSIBLE!

LET'S FACE IT, HELEN . . . YOU HAVE COMPETITION . . . DIVORCEES AT WORK, LOOKING FOR SECURITY AND A MAN . . . AND SOME DON'T CARE WHOSE HUSBAND THEY GET!
ALSO T.V. DOESN'T HELP, WITH BEAUTIFUL, SEDUCTIVE WOMEN THAT YOUR HUSBAND ENJOYS WATCHING.

WELL, I TRY TO MAKE MYSELF ATTRACTIVE BY USING CURLERS AND FACE CREAMS.
THAT'S FINE, HELEN, BUT WHY NOT TRY TO TAKE CARE OF YOUR BEAUTY TREATMENTS WHEN YOU'RE ALONE?

Wives submit yourselves unto your own husbands, as unto the Lord. For the husband is the head of the wife, even as Christ is the head of the church: and he is the saviour of the body. Therefore as the church is subject unto Christ, so let the wives be to their own husbands in every thing.

EPH. 5:22-24

WHEN YOU BOTH GIVE 100% OF YOURSELVES TO EACH OTHER . . . YOU WILL *THEN* BE MORE CONSIDERATE OF EACH OTHER!
IT'S THE LITTLE THINGS THAT COUNT, HELEN, LIKE TRYING TO LOOK NICE AND SMELLING GOOD.

AND ANOTHER POINT, HELEN . . . IF FRANK FAILS TO PERFORM, *NEVER* RIDICULE HIM! . . HE COULD BECOME INSECURE OVER HIS MANLINESS AND DEVELOP SOME REAL PROBLEMS . . .
SO BE SWEET AND TENDER AND YOU CAN OVERCOME THESE THINGS . . . . AND YOUR MARRIAGE WILL IMPROVE!
THANK YOU, MARK.

OH, MARK . . . WITH THE LORD'S HELP . . .
I'M GOING TO BE A GREAT WIFE!

AN EXCELLENT STUDY BOOK FOR MARRIED COUPLES IS . . . INTENDED FOR PLEASURE by Ed Wheat M.D. & Gaye Wheat, Fleming H. Revell Company.

CHAPTER EIGHT

FAREWELL

HEY, MOM, DAD SAID I COULDN'T GO SEE JIMMY BECAUSE I DIDN'T DO MY HOMEWORK!
THEN . . . THAT'S IT!

WHAT DO YOU MEAN "THAT'S IT!" CAN'T I GO?
NO!
YOUR FATHER IS THE HEAD OF THIS HOME AND WHATEVER HE SAYS, I GO ALONG WITH IT!

BRAD . . . THE BIBLE SAYS, "FOR THE HUSBAND IS THE HEAD OF THE WIFE, EVEN AS CHRIST IS THE HEAD OF THE CHURCH" . . . THAT'S FOUND IN EPHESIANS 5:23
WOW, MOM . . . YOU'RE REALLY STUDYING!
THEY DON'T NEED ME ANYMORE!

HEY, MARK . . . THE LORD REALLY TOUCHED MY HEART TODAY WHILE I WAS READING MY BIBLE AT LUNCH.
WHAT HAPPENED, FRANK?

I'VE WORRIED MYSELF SICK OVER A BUSINESS DEAL . . . AND I READ WHERE IT SAYS . . . "BE ANXIOUS FOR NOTHING" . . . PHIL. 4:6 AND I'VE BEEN SINNING WHEN I WORRY! . . . BECAUSE IT SHOWS A LACK OF FAITH!
THOU WILT KEEP HIM IN PERFECT PEACE, WHOSE MIND IS STAYED ON THEE: ISAIAH 26:3 SO I THROW MY PROBLEMS INTO THE LORD'S HANDS AND STOP WORRYING! . . . IT'S WONDERFUL!

*That he might sanctify and cleanse it with the washing of water by the word. EPH. 5:26

I'M LEAVING TOMORROW AND, FRANK, YOU HAVE BECOME *STRONG IN THE LORD . . . NOW I DON'T FEEL BAD ABOUT GOING!
EXCUSE ME, DADDY!
*EPH. 6:10

DADDY . . . I MET THIS WONDERFUL GUY AT SCHOOL . . . HE WANTS TO TAKE ME OUT THIS SATURDAY!
IS HE A REAL CHRISTIAN?
NO!

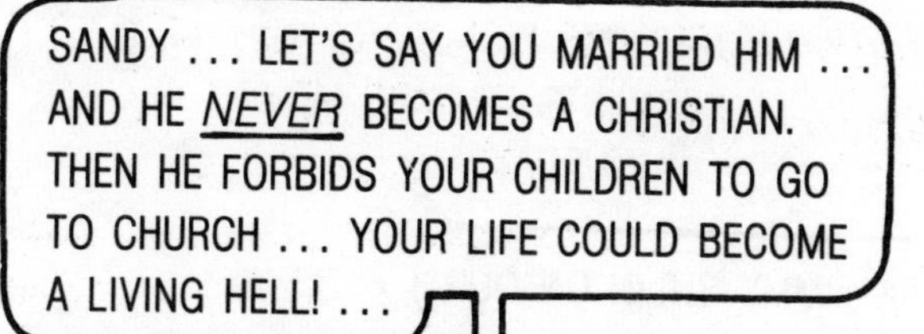
SANDY ... LET'S SAY YOU MARRIED HIM ... AND HE NEVER BECOMES A CHRISTIAN. THEN HE FORBIDS YOUR CHILDREN TO GO TO CHURCH ... YOUR LIFE COULD BECOME A LIVING HELL! ...
LET'S PRAY ABOUT IT, SANDY!

DAD, IF THE BIBLE FORBIDS IT, THEN I WON'T FIGHT IT! ... I'LL TELL HIM TO FORGET IT, UNTIL HE GETS SAVED!

HEY, DAD, CAN JIMMY SIT IN ON OUR BIBLE STUDY TONIGHT?
BRAD AND I ARE BROTHERS NOW . . . HE LED ME TO CHRIST!

MARK, GLORIA AND I HAVE SOMETHING WE WANT TO SHARE WITH YOU . . .
WHAT IS IT, BILLY?
WE BELIEVE THE LORD HAS REVEALED TO US THAT HE WANTS US IN THE MISSION FIELD
WE ARE CONVINCED HE WANTS US IN AFRICA . . . PRAY FOR US, MARK.

LAST DAY

MARK, BEFORE WE TAKE YOU TO THE AIRPORT, WE WANT TO PRAY!
CERTAINLY, FRANK!

THANK YOU, LORD, FOR ANSWERING PRAYER . . . KEEP THEM BUSY FOR YOU!
THANK YOU, FATHER . . . FOR SENDING MARK TO US!

NEXT DAY
KNOCK
KNOCK
BE PATIENT . . .
I'M COMING!

MRS. SMITH . . . WE HEARD YOU WEREN'T FEELING WELL SO WE CAME OVER TO GIVE YOU A HAND!
WELL, THAT'S REAL SWEET OF YOU!

MY STARS . . . I'M OVERWHELMED!

WE LOVE YOU, MRS. SMITH, AND SO DOES JESUS . . . WOULD YOU LIKE TO GO TO CHURCH WITH US NEXT SUNDAY? . . . AND HAVE DINNER WITH US?
I'D LOVE TO! . . . YOU KNOW SOMETHING?
WHAT, MRS. SMITH?

I'VE KNOWN A LOT OF CHURCH GOERS . . . BUT YOU'RE THE FIRST *REAL* CHRISTIANS I'VE EVER MET!
THANK YOU, LORD JESUS!
THE END